8.95

21ST CENTURY HITS

WISE PUBLICATIONS
PART OF THE MUSIC SALES GROUP

LONDON / NEW YORK / PARIS / SYDNEY / COPENHAGEN / BERLIN / MADRID / TOKYO

PUBLISHED BY
WISE PUBLICATIONS
14-15 BERNERS STREET, LONDON, W1T 3LJ, UK.

EXCLUSIVE DISTRIBUTORS:
MUSIC SALES LIMITED
DISTRIBUTION CENTRE, NEWMARKET ROAD, BURY ST EDMUNDS,
SUFFOLK, IP33 3YB, UK.
MUSIC SALES PTY LIMITED
120 ROTHSCHILD AVENUE, ROSEBERY, NSW 2018, AUSTRALIA.

ORDER NO. AM987822
ISBN 1-84609-782-7
THIS BOOK © COPYRIGHT 2006 BY WISE PUBLICATIONS,
A DIVISION OF MUSIC SALES LIMITED.

ARRANGED BY ZOE BOLTON.
EDITED BY FIONA BOLTON.
COVER PHOTOGRAPHS COURTESY OF LFI.
PRINTED IN THE EU.

TRAVIS

Sing

Words & Music by Fran Healy

Sing was the lead single from Travis' third studio album, *The Invisible Band*. The music video features a food fight between the band members, re-enacted when the Scottish indie-rockers performed the song on *Top Of The Pops*.

Hints & Tips: Where two quavers are joined by a slur (as in bar 11), place a slight emphasis on the first.

CHRISTINA AGUILERA

Beautiful

Words & Music by Linda Perry

This song it taken from the album *Stripped*. A rousing female anthem, it is often described as a song of affirmation. You go girl!

Hints & Tips: The left hand must be played evenly. Try not to let one note stand out over any of the others. It is also important that the right hand is more prominent than the left as it carries the tune.

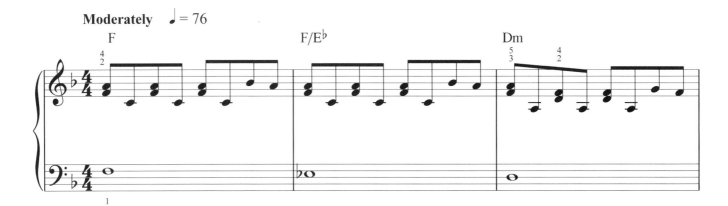

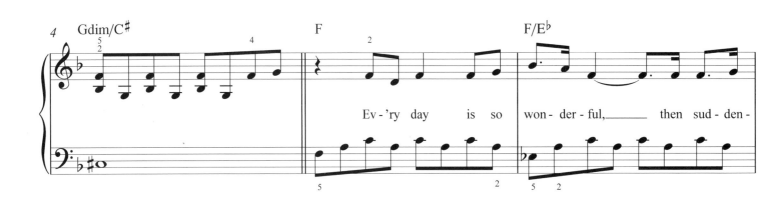

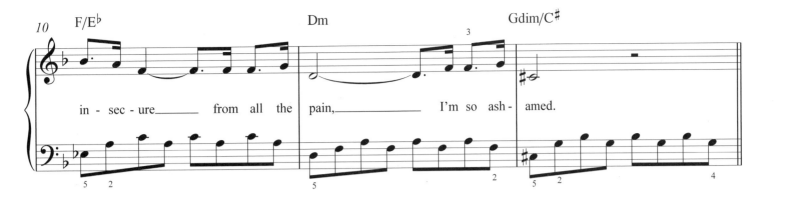

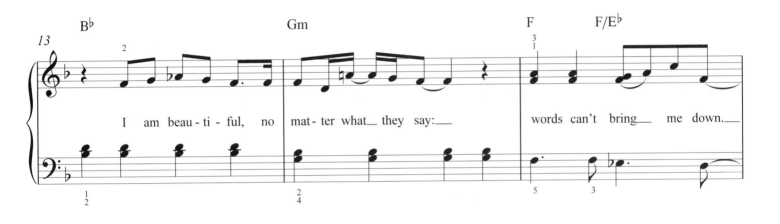

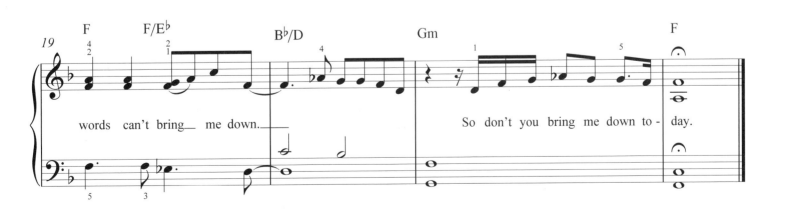

Born To Try

Words & Music by Delta Goodrem & Audius Mtawarira

Delta Goodrem found fame in both Australia and the UK through her role as aspiring singer-songwriter Nina Tucker in cult Australian soap *Neighbours*. This, her breakthrough single taken from her debut album *Innocent Eyes*, was even featured in the show.

Hints & Tips: The octave leaps in bars 4 and 6 are probably the hardest thing in this piece. Practise these bars before you play the piece through and prepare yourself by looking ahead as you approach them.

California

Words & Music by Alex Greenwald & Jason Schwartzman

This song, which received major attention when used as the theme song for hit TV show *The O.C.*, is about driving to a concert along the U.S. Route 101. Somewhat ironically, U.S. Route 101 does not actually extend as far south as Orange County!

Hints & Tips: There needs to be a real contrast between the two halves of this song. The opening 18 bars should be quiet and melancholy, building into the much louder chorus from bar 21.

Can't Get You Out Of My Head

Words & Music by Cathy Dennis & Rob Davis

Another Australian pop princess whose career was launched when she starred in *Neighbours*, Kylie cemented her comeback with this dance track. Taken from her eighth album *Fever*, and a far cry from her earlier Stock, Aitken & Waterman days, it reached No. 1 in no less than forty countries.

Hints & Tips: Rushing off-beat quavers (as featured in the left hand) is an easy trap to fall into. Take extra care to ensure these notes are correctly placed throughout the piece.

KATIE MELUA

The Closest Thing To Crazy

Words & Music by Mike Batt

This debut single from elfin chanteuse Katie Melua was penned by Mike Batt whose other hits include *Bright Eyes* and *The Wombling Song*! Katie herself was born in Georgia and moved to Belfast when she was nine.

Hints & Tips: There are a lot of changes of time signature in this song.
They should be no problem provided you feel a steady crotchet (quarter note) pulse throughout

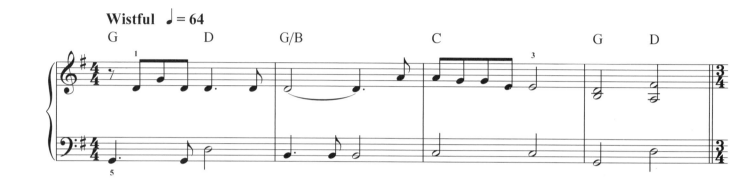

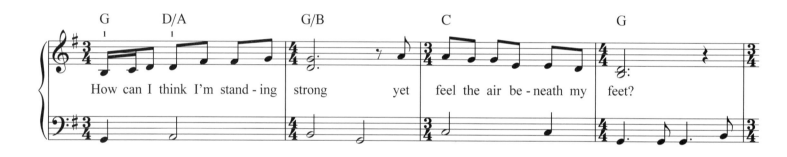

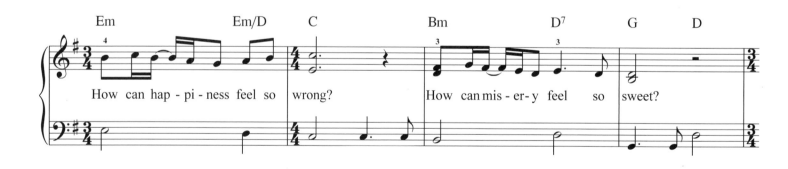

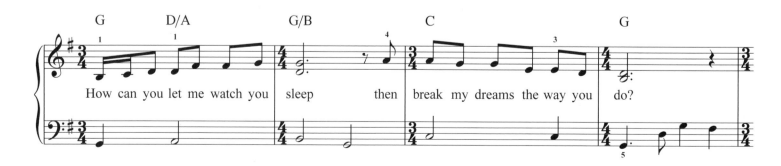

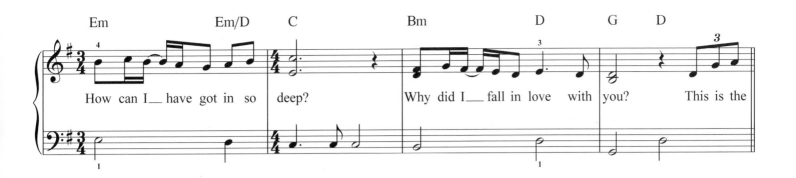

How can I— have got in so deep? Why did I— fall in love with you? This is the

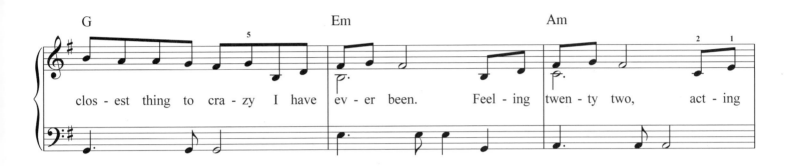

clos - est thing to cra - zy I have ev - er been. Feel - ing twen - ty two, act - ing

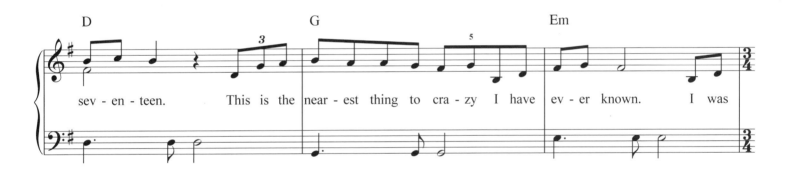

sev - en - teen. This is the near - est thing to cra - zy I have ev - er known. I was

nev - er cra - zy on my own and now I know— that there's a link be - tween the

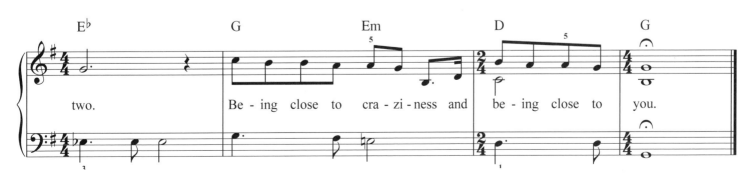

two. Be - ing close to cra - zi - ness and be - ing close to you.

Crazy

Words & Music by Thomas Callaway, Brian Burton, Gianfranco Reverberi & Gian Piero Reverberi

DJ/producer Danger Mouse and rapper/singer Cee-Lo (a.k.a. Gnarls Barkley) made history in March 2006 when *Crazy* became the first ever single to top the UK singles chart on download sales alone, having been released online a week prior to its release as a CD single.

Hints & Tips: Practise this piece slowly at first, paying careful attention to the fingerings. If your hand cannot stretch to the octave spread required in bars 16 – 21 just play the top notes starting with your thumb on the C.

Don't Know Why

Words & Music by Jesse Harris

Taken from her hugely successful debut album *Come Away With Me*, which sold 20 million copies worldwide, *Don't Know Why* was named Song of the Year at the Grammy Awards in 2003, one of eight Grammy Awards picked up by Norah Jones that year.

Hints & Tips: There are many accidentals (sharps, flats and natural signs) in this piece in addition to the two flats in the key signature. Remember that accidentals remain applicable for the whole of the bar in which they occur.

Don't Stop Movin'

Words & Music by Simon Ellis, Sheppard Solomon & S Club 7

Don't Stop Movin' was thought by many to mark a transition from cheesy children's TV outfit to credible pop act for S Club 7, a notion surely reinforced by the rest of their 2001 album *Sunshine* which spawned this and two other chart topping singles.

Hints & Tips: Follow the fingerings closely and bring out the melody in the right hand throughout. Ensure the two notes (thirds) in the right hand (in bars 5 - 8) sound at exactly the same time.

Eternity

Words & Music by Robbie Williams & Guy Chambers

Released in 2001 with *The Road To Mandalay* as its B-side, *Eternity* was Robbie's first single not to feature on an album and his fourth UK No. 1. Having topped the singles chart twice more since, and with eight No. 1 selling albums now under his belt, it's no wonder he hasn't rejoined Take That, yet...

Hints & Tips: The position of the left hand changes a lot in this piece.
Keep the fingers close to the keys and move them as soon as possible to help you achieve a smooth line.

Evergreen

Words & Music by Jorgen Elofsson, Per Magnusson & David Kreuger

Having seen off competition in the form of Gareth Gates, Will Young, the winner of *Pop Idol 2002*, broke first-day sales records with this, his debut single.

Hints & Tips: Although it is not mentioned in the music, you could try to make the difference in character between the verse and chorus clear. The chorus (which starts in bar 15) can be played louder and more jubilantly whilst the verse can be more understated.

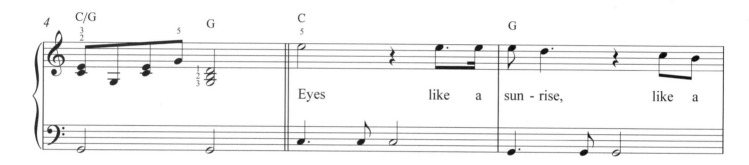

feels   like   love._____   I'm gon - na take this   mo - ment_   and make it last for -

-ev - er.   I'm gon - na give my   heart a - way___   and pray we'll stay___   to -

-geth - er.   'Cause you're the one   good   reas - on,   you're the on - ly

girl___ that I need,___ I'm gon - na take this night and make it ev - er - green.___

DANIEL BEDINGFIELD

If You're Not The One

Words & Music by Daniel Bedingfield

Daniel Bedingfield first graced the UK charts in 2001 with *Gotta Get Thru This*, a song he created using his own home studio. *If You're Not The One* was recorded a year later and spent 21 weeks in the charts including one week at No. 1.

Hints & Tips: Sort out the notes in the right hand first of all.
Then practise clapping or tapping the rhythm before putting everything together.

MICHAEL ANDREWS FEAT. GARY JULES

Mad World

Words & Music by Roland Orzabal

Originally written by Roland Orzabal of British band Tears for Fears, *Mad World* was covered by Gary Jules and
Michael Andrews for the film *Donnie Darko* and became the 2003 Christmas No. 1 in the UK.

Hints & Tips: Keep the tempo (speed) very steady.
Notice how the right hand notes often fall in between the left hand crotchets (quarter notes).

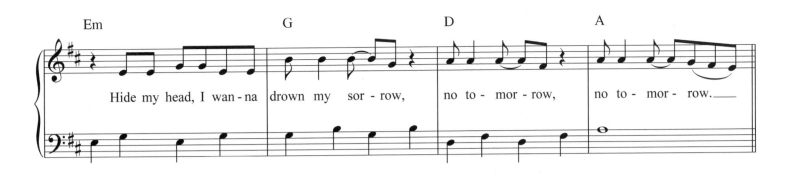

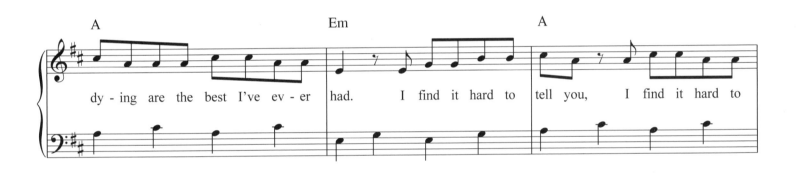

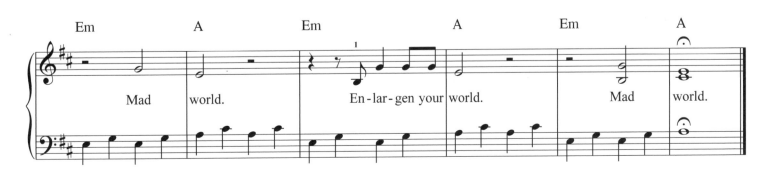

27

Oops!... I Did It Again

Words & Music by Max Martin & Rami

Like ...*Baby One More Time* before it, the music video for *Oops!... I Did It Again* was almost as popular as the song itself. In it Britney shows her maturity by donning a skin tight red catsuit rather than the school uniform many fans were accustomed to.

Hints & Tips: Watch out for the accidentals and cross-over fingerings in this piece. Also, take a careful look at where the left hand notes fall in relation to the right hand melody - mark it up if it helps you to do so.

Put Your Records On

Words & Music by John Beck, Steven Chrisanthou & Corinne Bailey Rae

The popularity of her second single *Put Your Records On* helped create a hype around Corinne Bailey Rae that saw her self-titled debut album reach the top spot on the UK album chart in its first week of release. Both the single and album feature her husband Jason Rae on alto saxophone.

Hints & Tips: This is a summery tune so keep it light, especially the left hand. Bring out the melody in the right hand so that is really 'sings' and play the chorus with spirit and confidence.

SUGABABES
Round Round

Words & Music by Brian Higgins, Keisha Buchanan, Mutya Buena, Heidi Range, Florian Pflueger, Felix Stecher, Robin Hofmann & Rino Spadavecchiaand

Round Round was the Sugababes' second consecutive UK No. 1 and one of the several of the group's hits produced by hits factory *Xenomania* - perhaps a more constant force behind the group than the members themselves.

Hints & Tips: Practise the right hand in bars 23 - 31 until your fingers are comfortable with the notes. Drop the tempo when you put the two hands together and make sure the two parts are fitting together neatly.

Dance Beat ♩ = 124

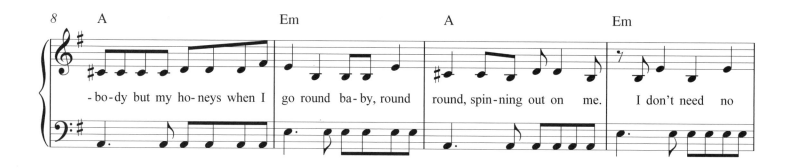

Somebody Told Me

Words & Music by Brandon Flowers, Dave Keuning, Mark Stoermer & Ronnie Van Nucci

Las Vegas rock band The Killers only formed in 2002, but by 2004 they had a No. 1 album (*Hot Fuss*) to their name. They were in fact named after a fictional band featured in the 2001 music video for *Crystal* by New Order which they went on to parody in the video for *Somebody Told Me*.

Hints & Tips: Try rocking between the notes in the left hand if you cannot reach them both at the same time.

Somewhere Only We Know

Words & Music by Tim Rice-Oxley, Tom Chaplin & Richard Hughes

Somewhere Only We Know was the first hit single from Keane, a band comprising Tom Chaplin (vocals), Tim Rice-Oxley (piano) and Richard Hughes (drums). All three were at school together in Hastings and named the band after a kind old local lady who'd looked after Tom when he was young.

Hints & Tips: Keep the repeated quavers (eighth notes) really steady, but don't play them too loudly, so that the tune is clearly heard.

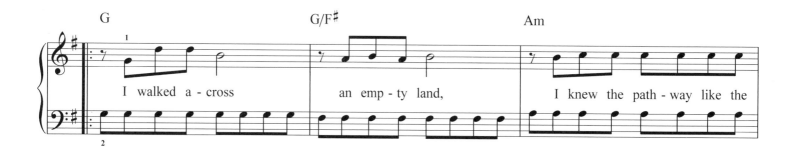

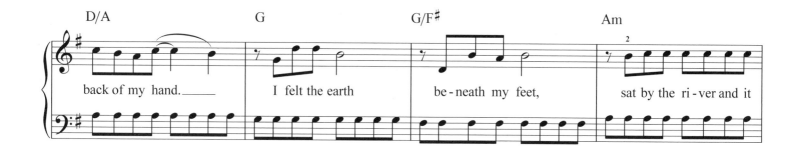

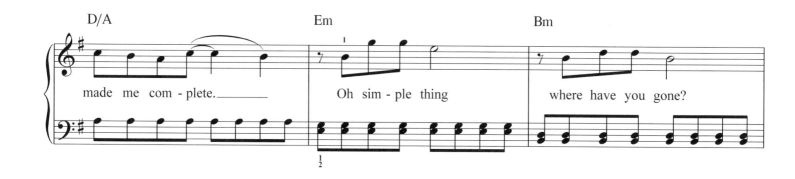

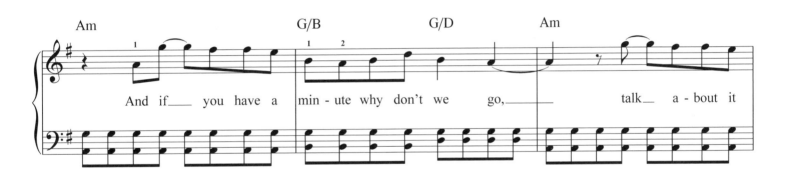

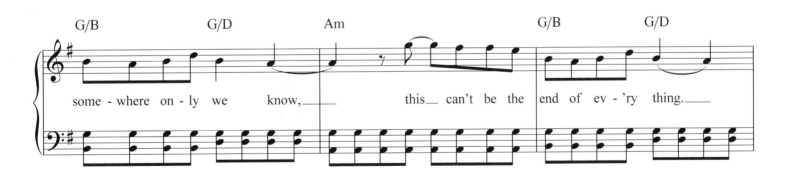

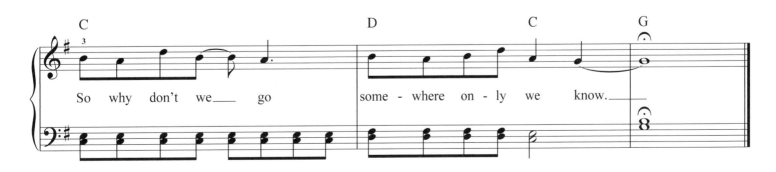

Star Girl

Words & Music by Thomas Fletcher, Daniel Jones, Harry Judd, Dougie Poynter, Daniel Carter, Julien Emery & Jason Perry

Star Girl topped the UK Chart in November 2006, becoming McFly's sixth No. 1. Originally a support act for Busted, they have developed their own style with influences from other great British bands such as The Beatles and Queen.

Hints & Tips: This song uses 'swung' rhythms, whereby the quavers in each pair are each given a slightly different length - either long-short or short-long. Listening to the recording will help you to understand this.

This Year's Love

Words & Music by David Gray

With his first three albums rejected by the major record companies, Daivd Gray made his fourth, *White Ladder*, in his London apartment. This song, from the album, became part of the soundtrack to a film of the same name.

Hints & Tips: If you think of 6/8 as having two dotted-crotchet (dotted-quarter note) beats in a bar, the rhythms in this piece will be much easier to count. You could mark out where the two beats occur in every bar.

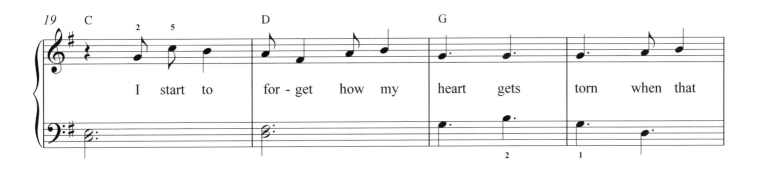

I start to   for - get how my   heart   gets   torn   when that

hurt   gets   thrown; feel - ing____ like I   can't____ go on.____

This   year's   love had   bet - ter last,____

1.

this   year's   love had   bet - ter last,____

2.

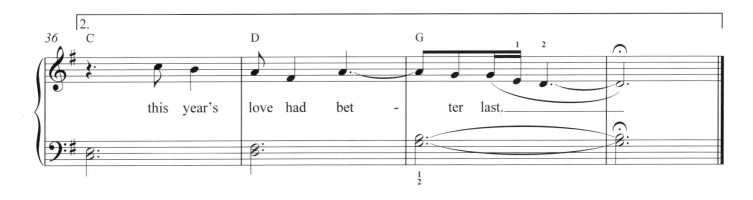

this   year's   love had   bet -   ter last.____

U2
Vertigo

Words & Music by David Evans, Adam Clayton, Paul Hewson & Laurence Mullen

Irish rock band U2, fronted by Bono, have been at the helm of the music industry since the 1970s, as well as being involved in numerous human rights campaigns in recent years. *Vertigo* was an international hit, winning three Grammy Awards; not that they were short of them as they already had 14!

Hints & Tips: Make sure the left hand does not rush through its quaver pattern. Also note how often the two hands move together and play the piece under tempo until you can achieve this cleanly.

Heavy Rock ♩ = 140

Lights go down, it's dark, the jun - gle is your

head, can't rule your heart. A feel - ing so much strong - er than a

thought, your eyes are wide and though your soul it can't be bought your mind can wan - der.

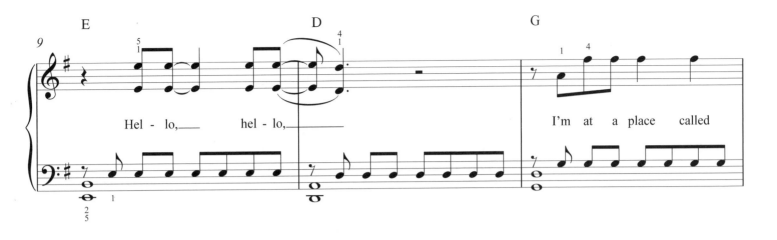

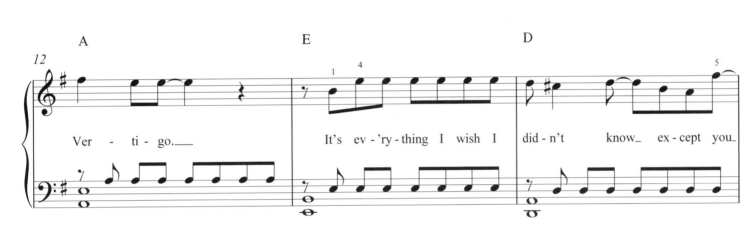

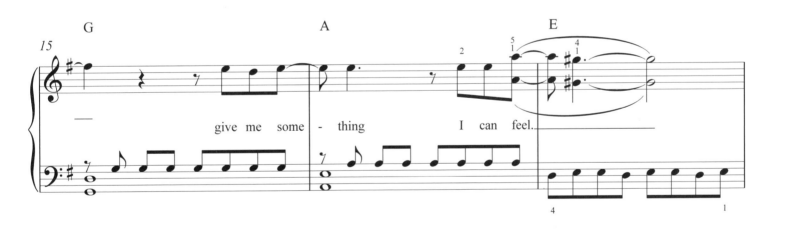

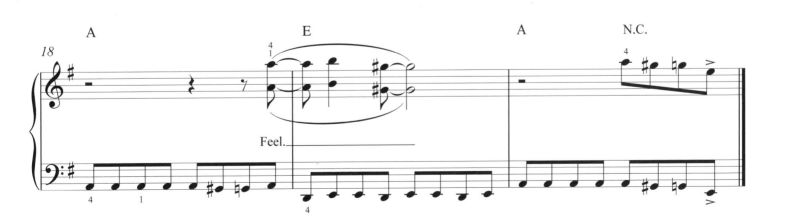

Wires

Words & Music by Joel Pott, Carey Willetts, Steve Roberts & Tim Wanstall

Written about the lead singer's daughter who was born prematurely, *Wires* won Athlete an Ivor Novello Award for 'Best Contemporary Song'. It also helped launch their second album *Tourist*, a follow-up to their Mercury Award-nominated debut *Vehicles & Animals*, to the top of the album chart.

Hints & Tips: The melody in bars 13 – 21 contains several leaps. Keep you right hand fingers 'glued' to the keys and ensure you play each note to its full value to help create a smooth melodic line.

down cor - ri - dors,__ through au - to - ma - tic doors; got to get to you,

got to see this through.___ I see hope is here in a plas - tic box.

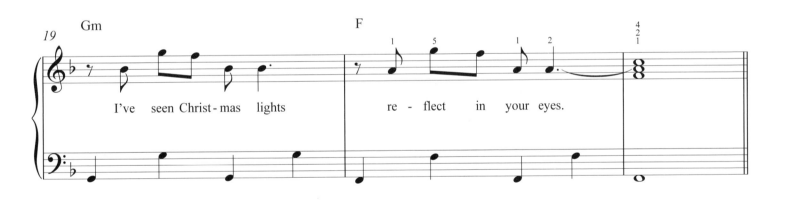

I've seen Christ - mas lights re - flect in your eyes.

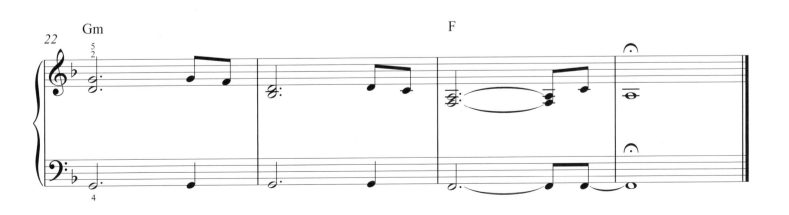

Yellow

Words & Music by Guy Berryman, Jon Buckland, Will Champion & Chris Martin

Yellow was the second single to be released from Coldplay's debut album *Parachutes* and is considered by many to be their breakthrough single. Rumour has it that the song title was inspired by the *Yellow Pages*!

Hints & Tips: The left hand should be played lightly and more softly than the right hand. However, placing a slight emphasise the first quaver of each bar will avoid the accompaniment sounding monotonous.

Slow Rock ♩ = 86

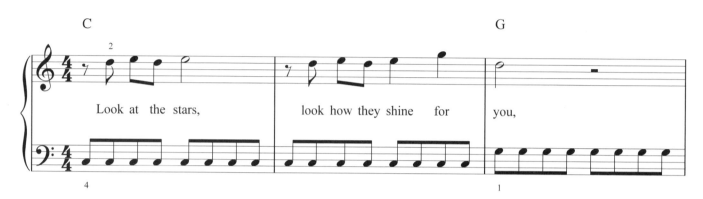

JAMES BLUNT

You're Beautiful

Words & Music by Sacha Skarbek, James Blunt & Amanda Ghost

You're Beautiful accomplished a feat rarely seen on the modern UK Singles Chart by climbing to No. 1 having initially entered it outside the Top Ten. With it ex-soldier Blunt also became the first British artist to top the American Billboard Hot 100 since Elton John's *Candle In The Wind 1997*.

Hints & Tips: Play this piece very smoothly (*legato*) by keeping your fingers close to the keys.

Ballad ♩ = 82

56789
10/09(171376)